A Dog Called Prince

written by Jay Dale

illustrated by Sherry Neidigh

Engage Literacy is published in 2013 by Raintree.
Raintree is an imprint of Capstone Global Library Limited, a company
incorporated in Engand and Wales having its registered office at 7 Pilgrim
Street, London, EC4V 6LB – Registered company number: 6695582
www.raintreepublishers.co.uk

Originally published in Australia by Hinkler Education, a division
of Hinkler Books Pty Ltd.
Text copyright © UpLoad Publishing Pty Ltd 2012
Illustration copyright © Hinkler Books Pty Ltd 2012

Written by Jay Dale
Lead authors Jay Dale and Anne Giulieri
Cover illustration and illustrations by Sherry Neidigh
Edited by Gwenda Smyth
UK edition edited by Dan Nunn, Catherine Veitch and Sian Smith
Designed by Susannah Low, Butterflyrocket Design

A Dog Called Prince
ISBN: 978 1 406 26514 9
10 9 8 7 6 5 4 3 2

Printed and bound in China by Leo Paper Products Ltd

Contents

Chapter 1
A New Pup

Tom peered down into the brown cardboard box. A small black and grey pup stretched and then yawned.

"Hey, Dad," Tom whispered. "He's waking up."

"Now, Tom," replied his father, "don't go all soft on me. He's a working dog. As soon as this pup's old enough, he'll be out the back with Matey."

Tom was disappointed. He gently put his hand
out to stroke the pup. The pup rolled over,
stretched and yawned again. Tom laughed,
"I think he wants me to tickle his tummy."

"Like I said," replied Dad, "he's not a pet.
He's a working dog."

"What are you going to call him?"
asked Tom, thoughtfully.

"Well," answered Dad, "this little pup's
father was the best working dog I've ever had.
He was like the king of all working dogs.
He could round up a herd of cows, moving
them from one paddock to another,
faster than any dog I've ever seen."

Tom scratched the pup's ears. "Prince!"
He smiled. "Let's call him Prince."

Tom and his dad lived on a large cattle farm
in Australia. His family had nearly 500 cows, and
Tom's dad was the best cattle dog trainer around.

"Come on, Tom," said Dad. "Bring Prince
down to the cattle yards. He can begin his
training today."

Chapter 2
A Good Cattle Dog

Prince sniffed the air and pricked his ears.
As soon as he smelt the cattle,
he became interested.

"Look at that!" smiled Dad, turning to Tom.
"We might have a good working dog here."
Tom peered through the fence as Dad let
Prince into the yard with Matey.

"We'll only give him a minute or two with
the cattle today," said Dad. "We don't want
to frighten him." Prince followed Matey into
the yard.

"Go behind," Dad said to Matey. Matey crept low behind a large cow. As Matey came close to the cow's back legs, she nipped its heels to try to move it forward. The cow kicked its legs out, just missing Matey's head as she dropped to the ground. Prince watched excitedly from the fence. He yapped noisily as the cow was herded through the gate and into the next yard.

"Grab Prince," called Dad to Tom.
"He's getting a bit excited."

Tom quickly reached through the fence to
grab Prince's collar. But before he could get
a hold, Prince leapt forward and raced
behind a large cow.

"Prince," yelled Tom, "get back!" But it was too late. Prince nipped the cow's heels. In a flash, the cow's back legs kicked out — hitting Prince in the leg! A loud yelp filled the air as the injured pup limped under the fence and out of the yard.

"Prince!" called Tom, racing after the terrified pup.

Prince finally stopped behind the old shed. He lay there shivering and shaking, and licking his injured leg.

"Oh, Prince!" cried Tom. "What have you done?"

Dad came racing around to the back of the shed. "I told you to grab that pup," he said angrily.

"I'm sorry," said Tom. "I wasn't quick enough."

"Well, it's too late now!" said Dad, coldly.
"That pup is not much use to us now.
He's most likely broken his leg. And even
if his leg gets better, he'll be too terrified
to round up the cows."

Tom looked at Dad. Suddenly, everything became clear. Dad was the kind of man who only kept dogs that could work.

"Dad," begged Tom, "please give him a chance. I'll take good care of him. I'll see to his leg and I'll train him to be the best dog we've ever had. I've got the summer holidays to train him."

Dad looked from Tom to the pup. Prince was still shaking and huddled close to Tom. Dad shook his head slowly, as if trying to make up his mind. "Okay," he said, finally. "You can keep him over summer. If he can't be trained by then, he'll have to go."

Tom carried the frightened pup onto the verandah and laid him gently on an old grey blanket. Dad came over and carefully felt his injured leg. The pup gave a sharp yelp.

"It's broken all right," said Dad. "We'll have to bandage it into place. The vet in Kingston has gone away for two months. We'll have to take care of this pup ourselves."

Chapter 3
Training Prince

The bandage stayed in place over the following weeks, and as Tom did his jobs around the farm, Prince would slowly limp behind him. It was during this time that Tom started Prince's training. He taught him always to follow behind, to come when he was called, and to "stay" when he was told.

Prince was clever and easy to train, and as
Dad watched from a distance, he secretly hoped
Tom would be able to train Prince.

Six weeks after Prince had broken his leg,
Dad took the bandage off. Prince raced around
the yard, a slight limp the only thing holding
him back.

"His leg has healed," said Dad, "but the real
test is yet to come!"

"Dad," said Tom in the last week of the holidays, "I think Prince is ready to go down to the cattle yards."

Dad gazed at Tom. "Are you sure, son?" he asked.

Tom gave a little smile. "We have to do it some time. Prince understands everything I tell him now. We just have to make sure he's brave enough to get back in with the cows."

Dad called to Matey, and then turned to Tom. "Okay," he said, "let's go. I've got three cows in the yard. We can test Prince out on those."

Matey ran straight into the first yard and began rounding up the three cows. Prince hung back. He stayed close to Tom, sitting quietly behind his heels. Dad called Prince into the yard but Prince didn't move. Dad lifted an eyebrow at Tom. He didn't need to say anything. His look said it all.

Chapter 4
Last Chance for Prince

"Dad," said Tom, "I'll bring Prince into the yard on his lead. He might feel safer if I go in with him."

Tom led Prince into the yard. Prince took one look at the big cows and nervously hid behind Tom. Tom patted him. "Please, boy," he encouraged, "you have to be brave. You have to show Dad that you really are a prince among dogs."

Prince tipped his head to one side as if he understood. He sniffed the air. The smell of the cows filled his nostrils. He looked at Matey crouching low, ready to follow Dad's instructions. Tom undid the lead and let Prince go.

At first, Prince carefully moved out from behind Tom's heels. Then he sniffed the air and something took over. As Matey raced out to nip the cows' back legs, so did Prince. He nipped a big red cow's heels. Then he crouched low as the cow's back legs kicked out. He nipped again and missed the cow's second kick. A large smile spread across Tom's face. "Come!" he called. "Come, Prince." At once, Prince left the cow and came back to Tom. Tom leant down and patted his dog. "Well done!" he encouraged. "Well done!"

Tom smiled at Dad. "He's a prince after all."

"Yes!" said Dad, "and you're one of the finest dog trainers I've seen."

But there was only one thing on Tom's mind. "Can he stay, Dad?"

Dad smiled in reply. "Of course he can. He's a working dog now."